The Story of MOSES

Illustrated by Pascale Lafond

1. Have no other gods.

2. Worship only God.

3. Honor God's name.

4. Honor God's day.

5. Honor your parents.

6. Do not kill.

7. Be faithful in marriage.

8. Do not steal.

9. Do not lie.

10. Do not be jealous.

Moses was an Israelite boy who was born in Egypt. At the time Moses was born, the Pharaoh, who was the ruler of Egypt, ordered that all Israelite boys should be killed. His mother was afraid for Moses, so she sent him down the river in a basket.

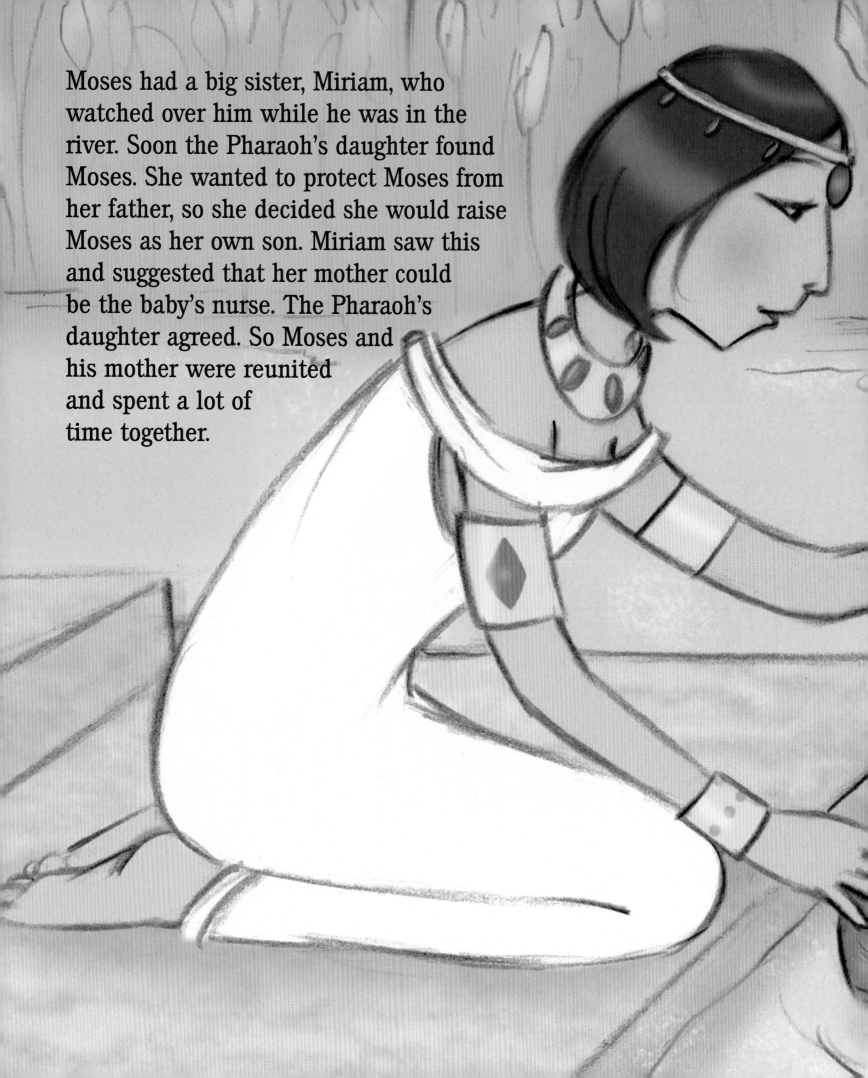

Moses had a big sister, Miriam, who watched over him while he was in the river. Soon the Pharaoh's daughter found Moses. She wanted to protect Moses from her father, so she decided she would raise Moses as her own son. Miriam saw this and suggested that her mother could be the baby's nurse. The Pharaoh's daughter agreed. So Moses and his mother were reunited and spent a lot of time together.

When Moses was growing up, the Israelite people were slaves in Egypt. This meant they had to work very hard night and day with almost no rest and no money. It was a very hard life.

When Moses grew into a man, he left Egypt. He eventually ended up in a place called Midian. There he stopped to rest by a well where seven sisters were getting water for their sheep. Along came a group of men who tried to push the women aside. Moses helped the women, telling the men to wait their turn. This was both brave and kind.

When the women told this story to their father, he invited Moses to live with them. There he became a shepherd. He lived there for a long time and eventually even married one of these sisters.

But Moses never forgot about the Israelites struggling in Egypt.

Back in Egypt, life was still very hard for the Israelites. They were still forced to work as slaves. They prayed to God for help.

One day, while Moses was out looking after some sheep, he noticed a bush on fire. Even though it was on fire, there was no smoke, and the bush was not burning up. As Moses approached the bush to look closer, a voice came from inside it. It was the voice of God. God spoke to Moses and told him to go back to Egypt, to speak to the Pharaoh, and ask him to let the Israelite people go free.

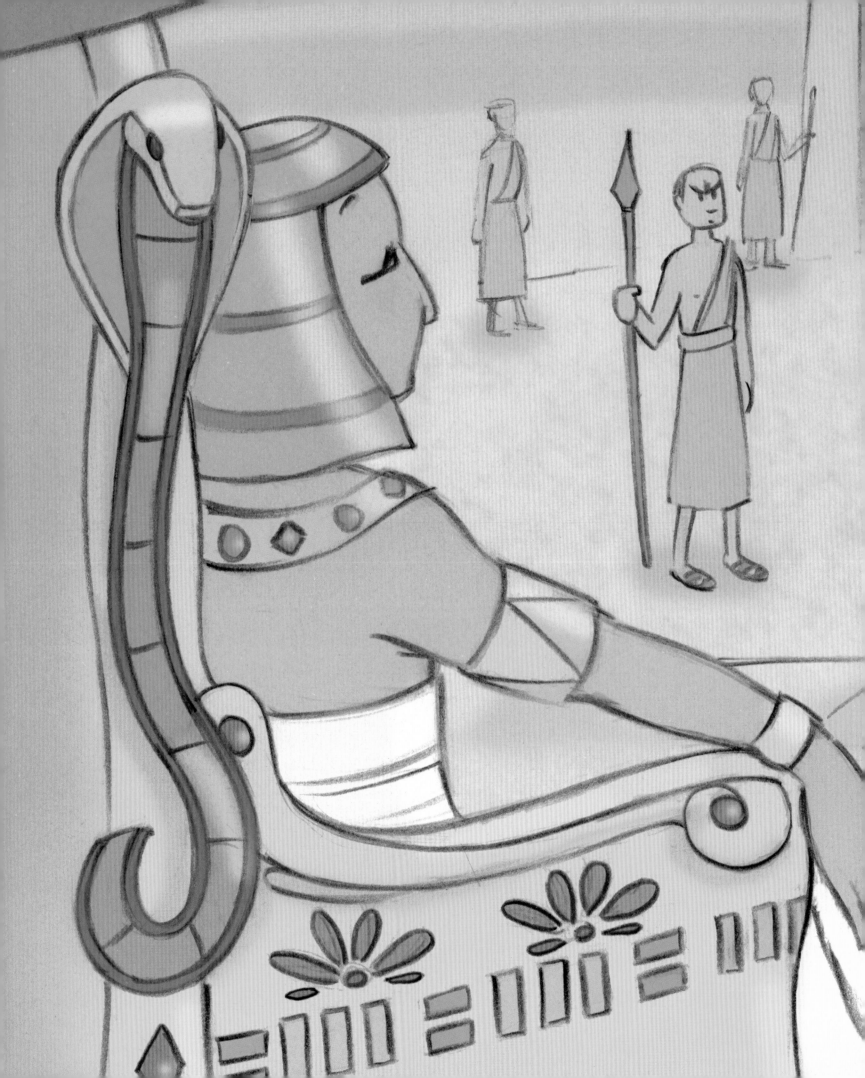

Moses traveled back to Egypt. He went to see the Pharaoh and told him that God wanted him to let the Israelite people go free. But the Pharaoh refused.

God worked with Moses to try to change the Pharaoh's mind. They performed acts that should have proven to the Pharaoh that Moses was speaking God's will, but the Pharaoh wouldn't listen. So God brought many plagues on Egypt like frogs, locusts, hail, and darkness. There were so many plagues that the people of Egypt couldn't even leave their homes.

When the Pharaoh finally realized that God and Moses would not give up, he decided to let the Israelite people go free. When Moses visited with him again, the Pharaoh told Moses they could go. Moses was not confident the Pharaoh would stick to his word, so he wanted to leave Egypt right away.

Moses and the Israelites hurried out of Egypt. But the Pharaoh did change his mind, and he sent his army to bring the Israelite people back to Egypt. As the army approached, God parted the Red Sea so the Israelite people could escape. Once they were safe, He closed the passage through the sea so the army could not follow them.

Once they escaped from the Pharaoh in Egypt, the Israelites spent many days and nights in the desert searching for the Promised Land. It was very hard, but God watched over them. Eventually, they came to Mount Sinai.

God wanted to help His people know the right way to live. So God called Moses up onto Mount Sinai, and there He gave Moses the Ten Commandments. He told Moses to share these commandments with His people. The Ten Commandments tell us how to live in God's love.

Moses told God that the Israelites
would follow the Ten Commandments.

1. Have no other gods.

2. Worship only God.

3. Honor God's name.

4. Honor God's day.

5. Honor your parents.

Moses lived to be very old. He devoted his life to helping the Israelites find their Promised Land and teaching them how to live in God's love. Moses wrote a song for the people. It was all about the love of God and how God had helped them all throughout the years. Before Moses died, God showed him the Promised Land. Moses said, "Thank You, Lord."